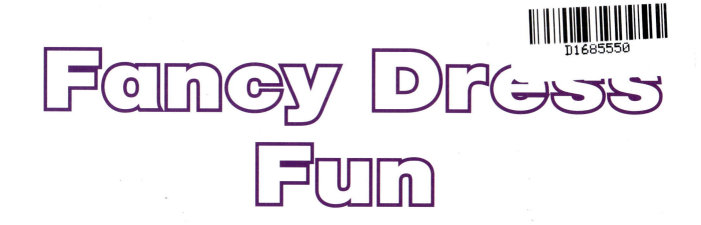

Fancy Dress Fun

Story by Neil Griffiths

Illustrated by Mary Hall

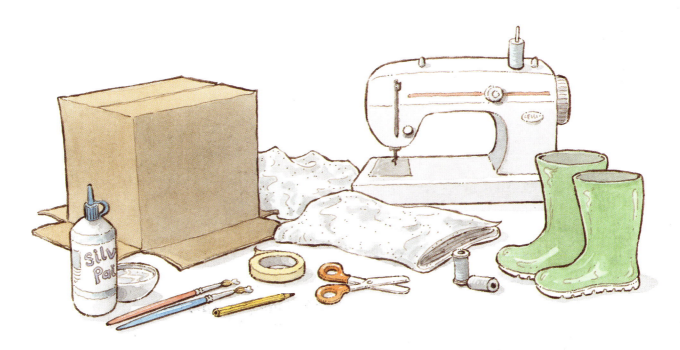

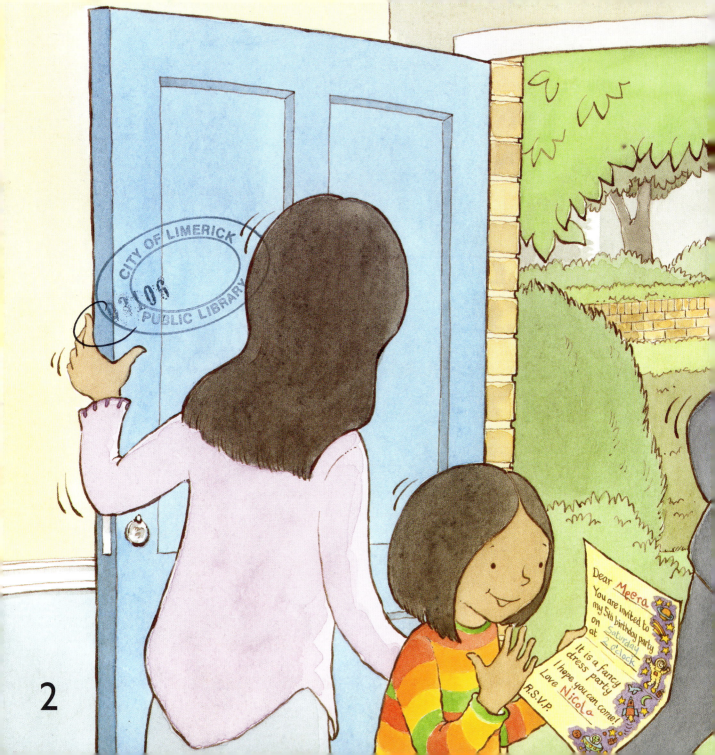

Dear Meera

You are invited to my 5th birthday party on Saturday at 2 o'clock

It is a fancy dress party
I hope you can come!
Love Nicola
R.S.V.P.

2

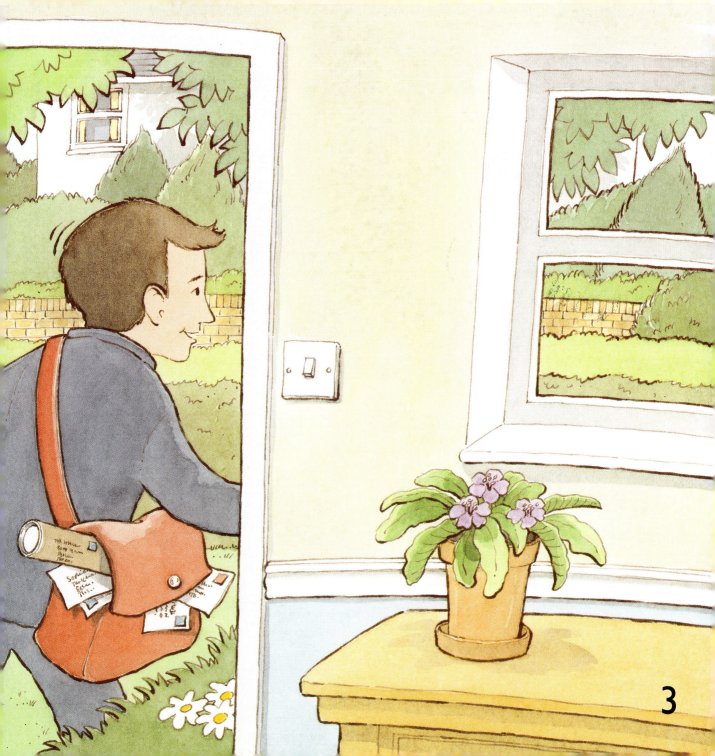

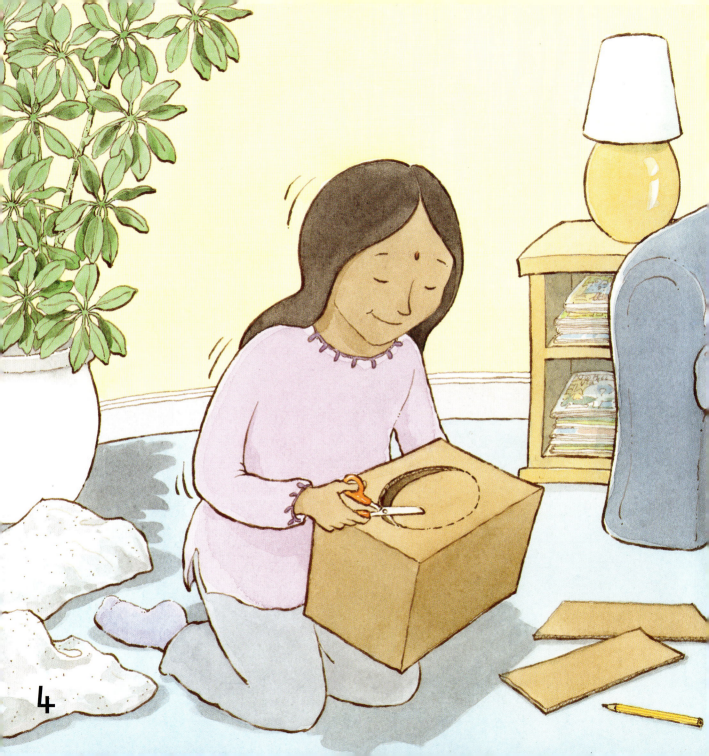

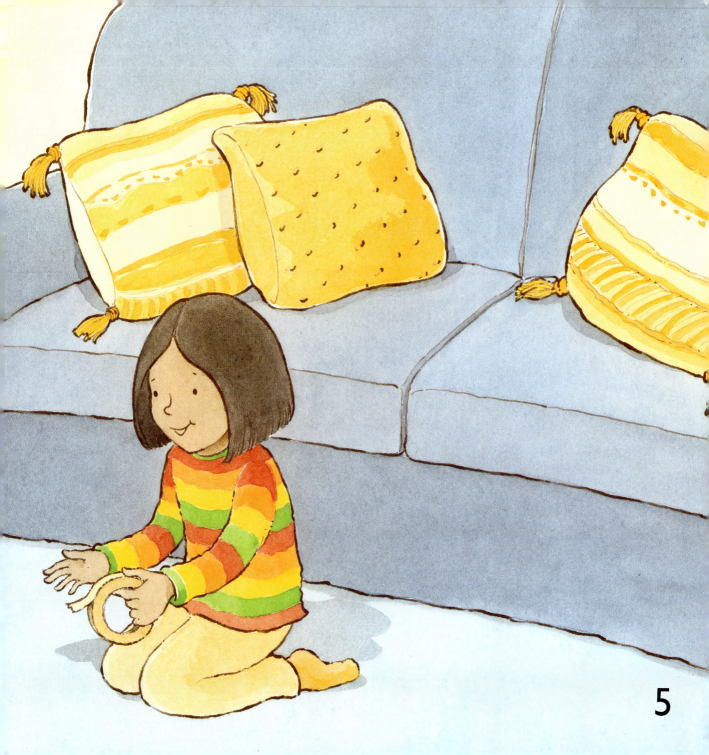

5

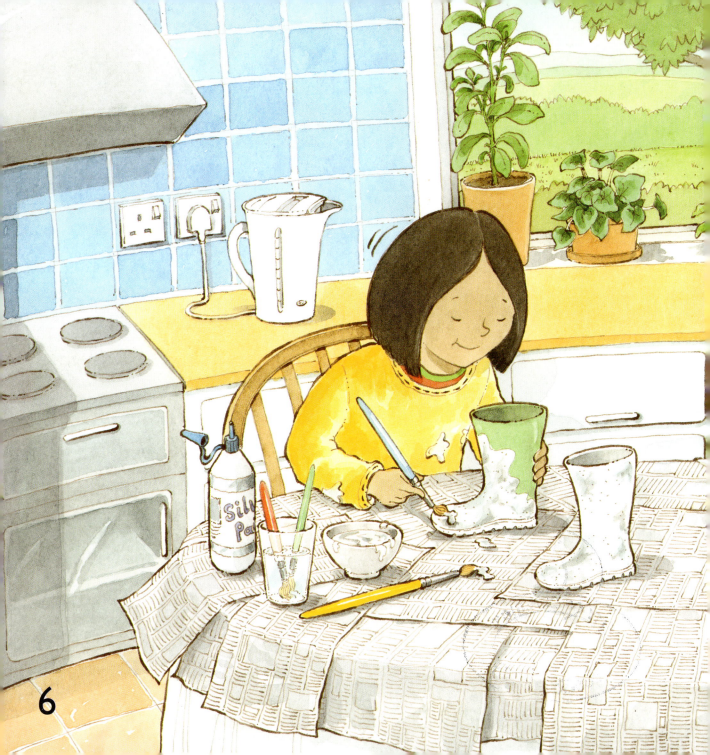

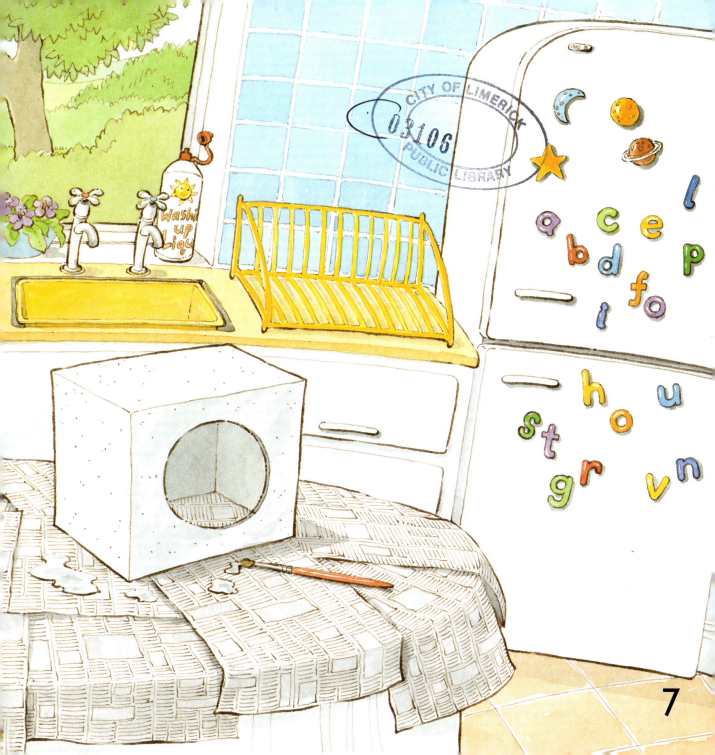

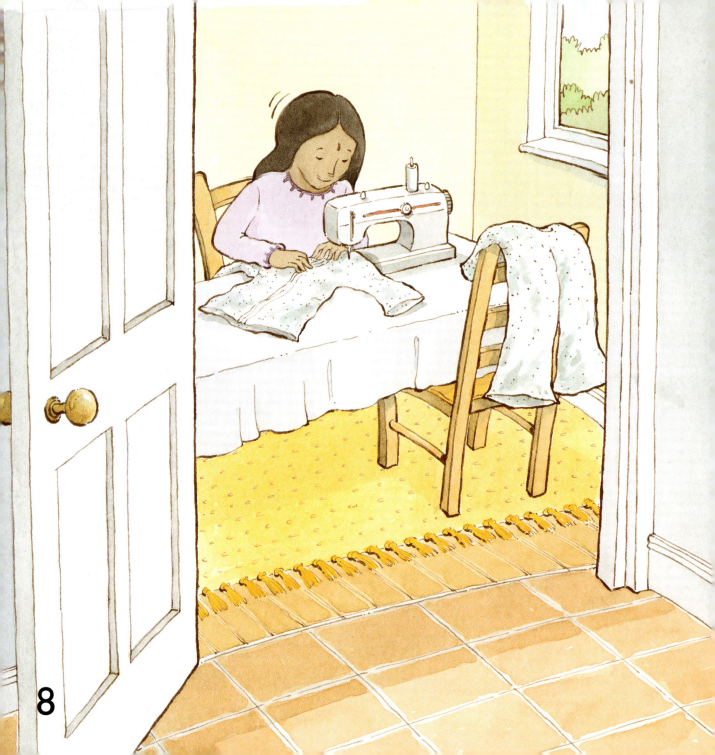

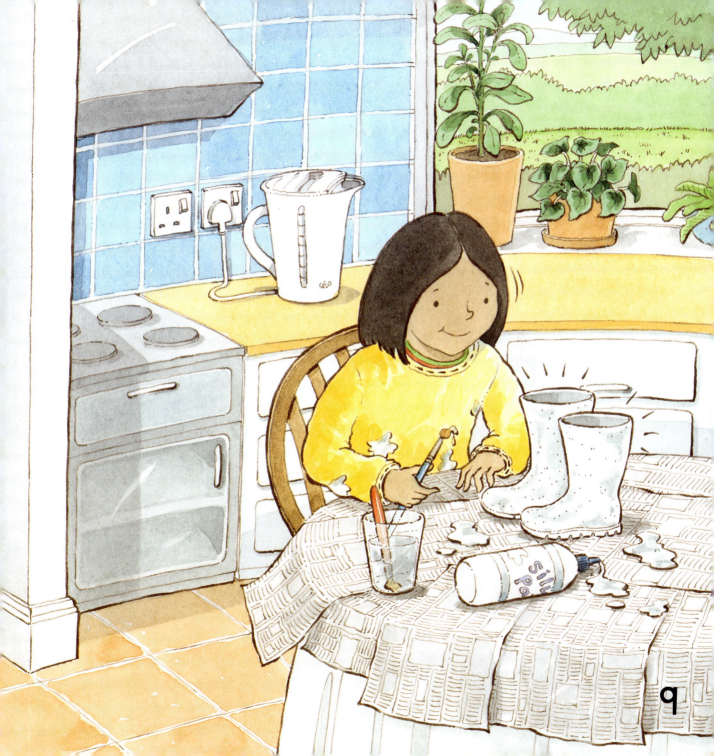

q

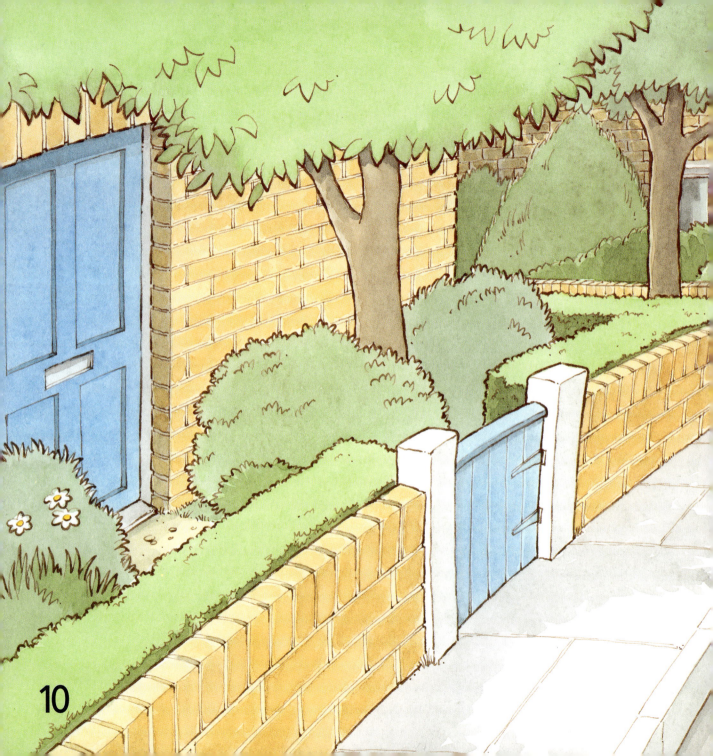

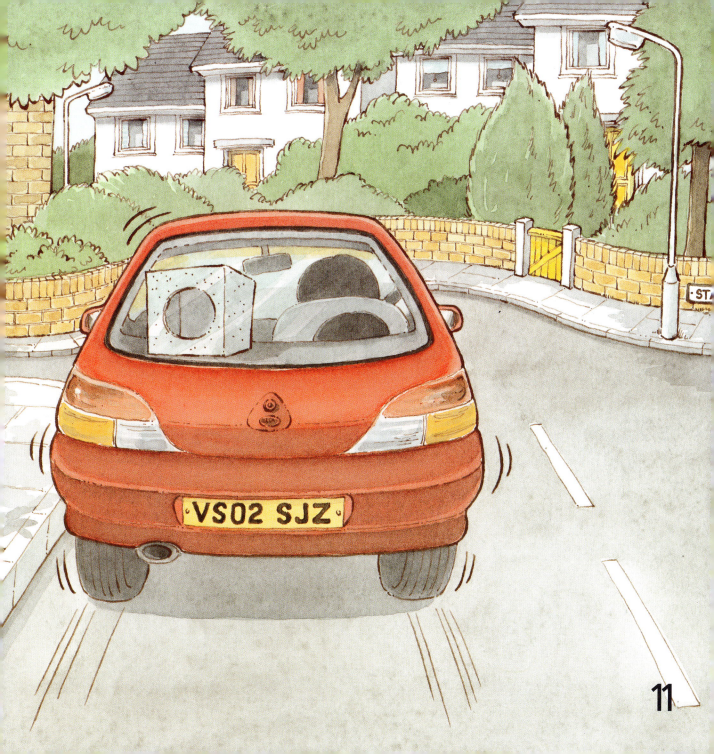

11

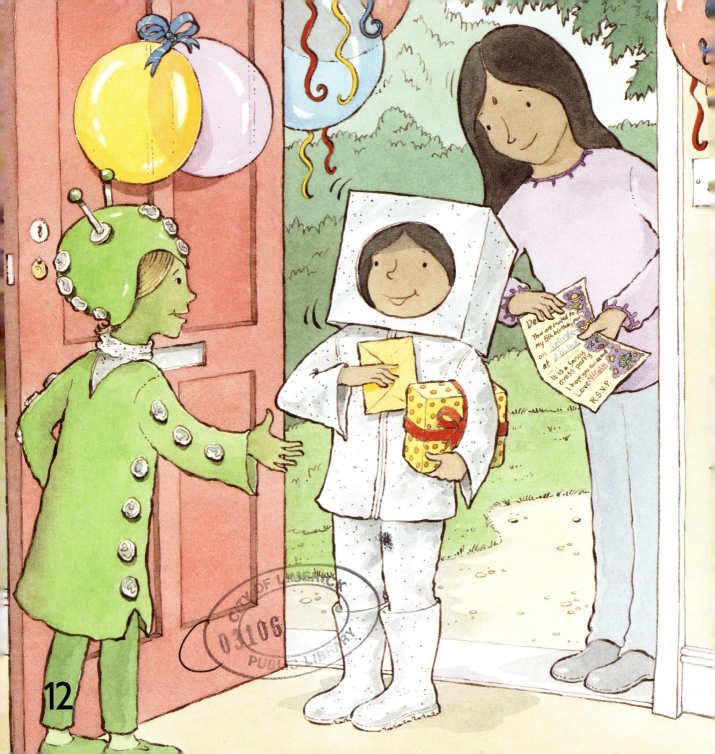

12